Mighty Mighty **MONSTERS**

THE MISSING MUMMY

www.raintreepublishers.co.uk
Visit our website to find out
more information about
Raintree books.

To order:
☎ Phone 0845 6044371
🖨 Fax +44 (0) 1865 312263
📧 Email myorders@raintreepublishers.co.uk

Customers from outside the UK please telephone +44 1865 312262

Raintree is an imprint of Capstone Global Library Limited,
a company incorporated in England and Wales having its registered
office at 7 Pilgrim Street, London, EC4V 6LB
– Registered company number: 6695582

First published by Stone Arch Books in 2010
First published in the United Kingdom in paperback in 2012
The moral rights of the proprietor have been asserted.

Edited by Siân Smith
Originated by Capstone Global Library Ltd
Printed and bound in China

ISBN 978 1 406 24227 0 (paperback)
16 15 14 13
10 9 8 7 6 5 4 3 2

British Library Cataloguing in Publication Data

THE MISSING MUMMY

created by
Sean O'Reilly

illustrated by
Arcana Studio

In a strange corner of
the world known as
Transylmania . . .

Legendary monsters were born.

WELCOME TO
TRANSYLMANIA

But long before their frightful fame, these
classic creatures faced fears of their own.

To take on terrifying teachers and homework horrors,
they formed the most fearsome friendship on Earth . . .

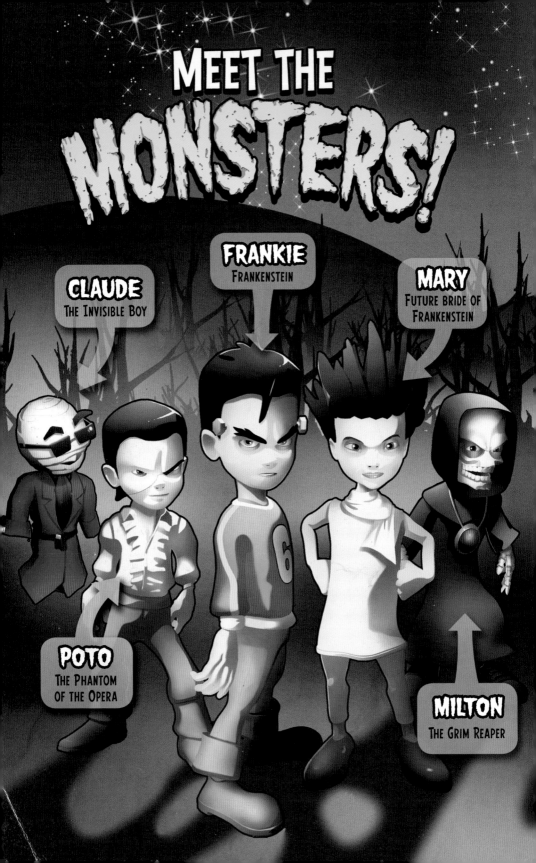

Settle down, class. We are guests of the museum today.
You will be under constant supervision.
You're here to learn, not to have fun!
So let's have a good day out there, children.

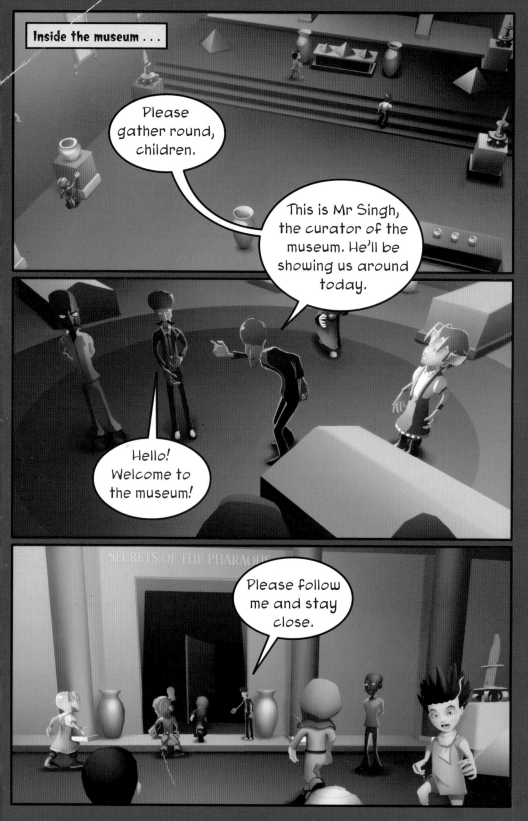

As you may know, the ancient Egyptians held their gods in the utmost respect.

Fascinating!

Magnificent!

Just wait... the best is yet to come!

Pharaohs ruled ancient Egypt. The pharaohs were more than just rulers, however.
They were living monuments of Egypt.
Wow! I've seen a lot of coffins, but this tomb takes the cake!

One famous pharaoh was King Tut.
King Tut was ruling an entire kingdom when he was no older than you are now.

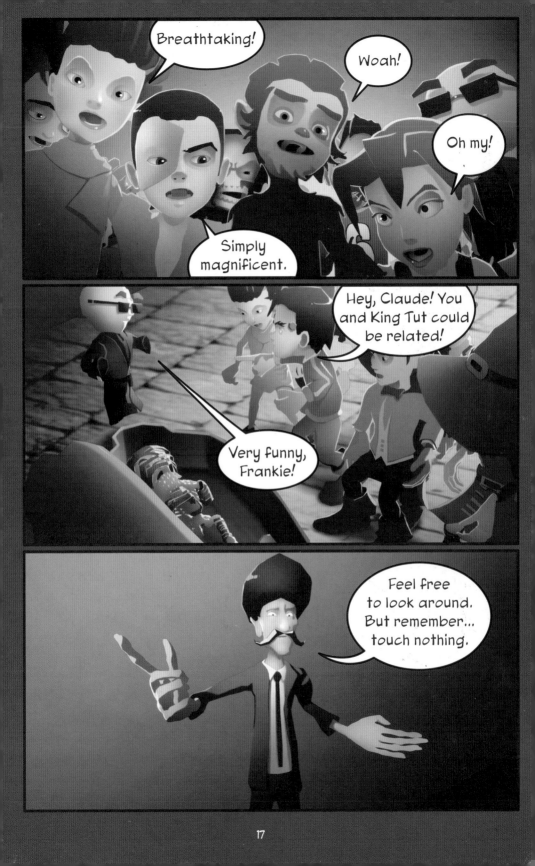

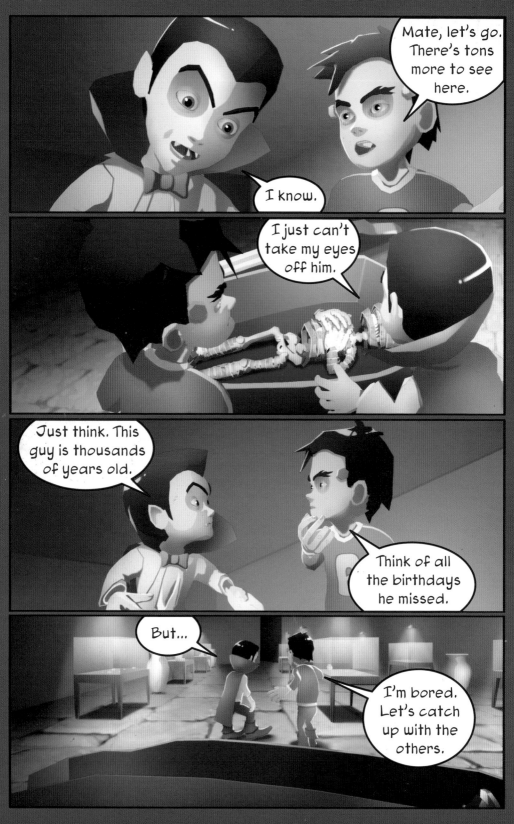

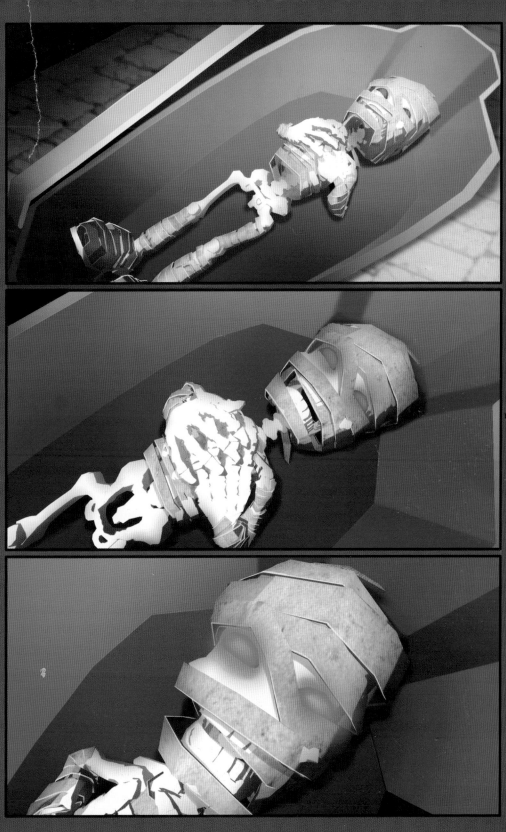

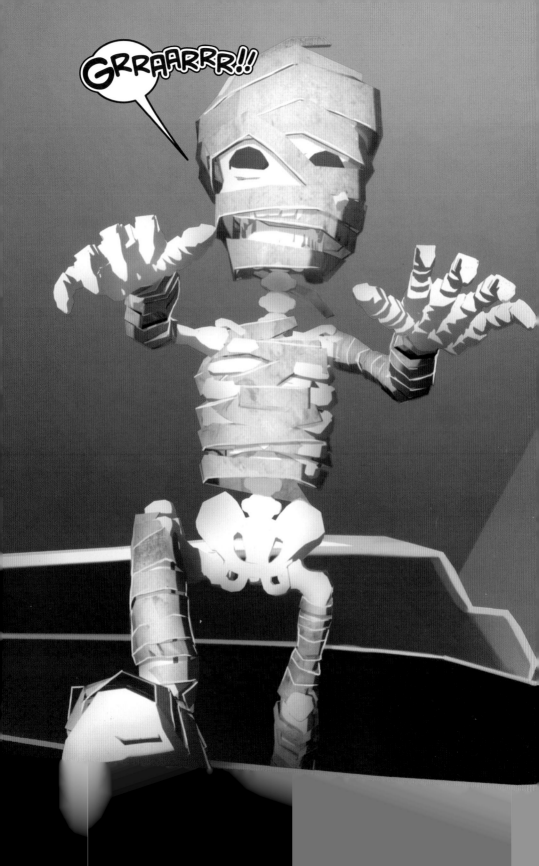

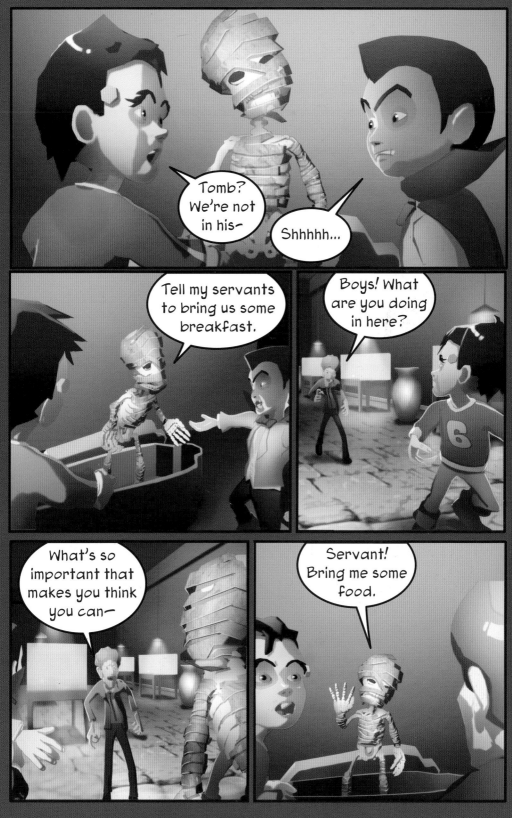

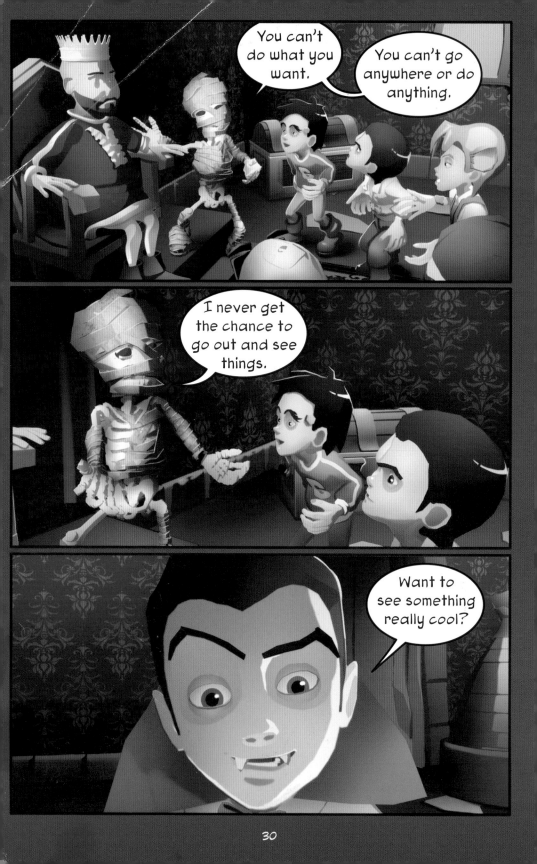

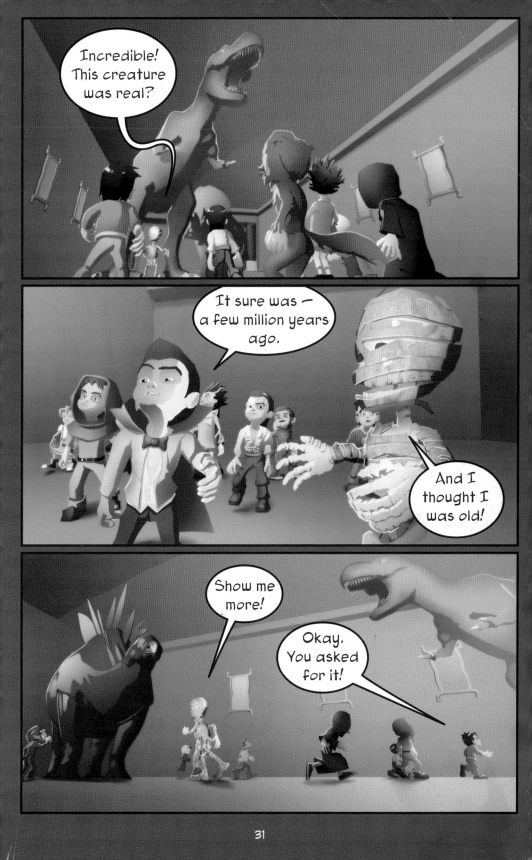

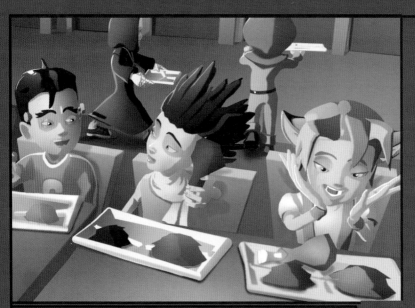

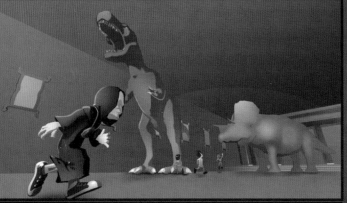
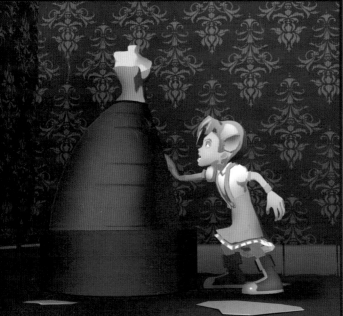

CRUNCH!! CRUNCH!!

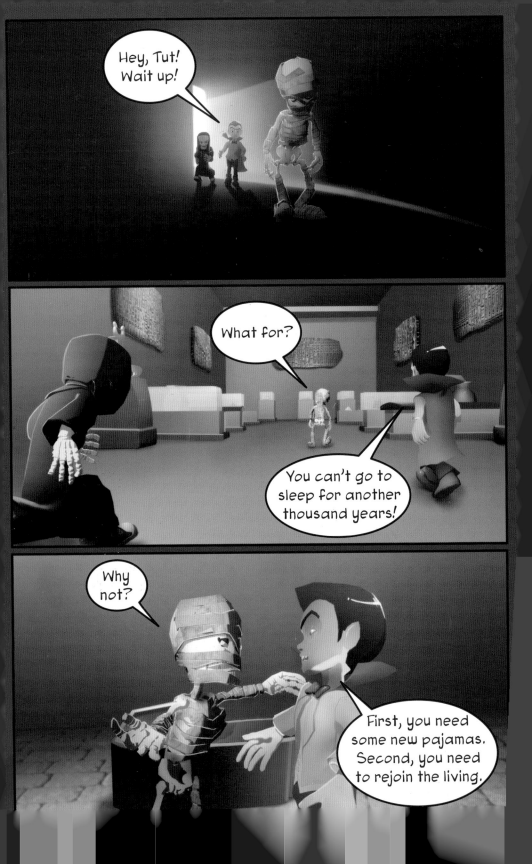

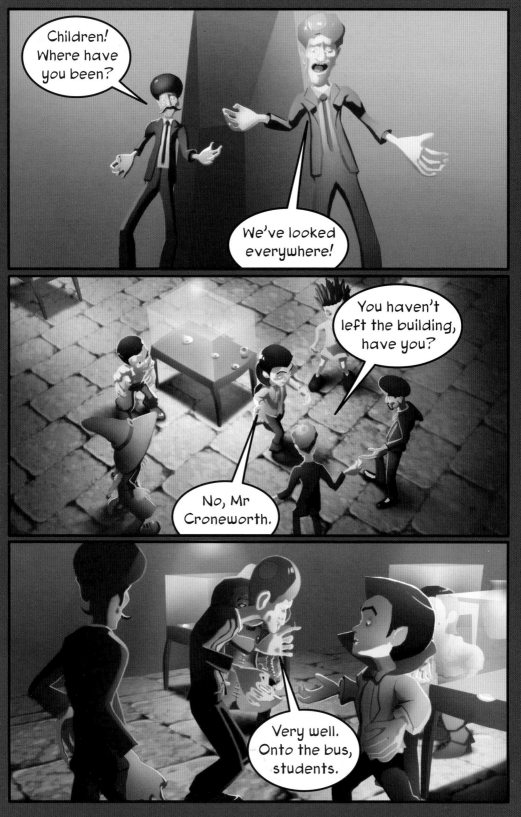

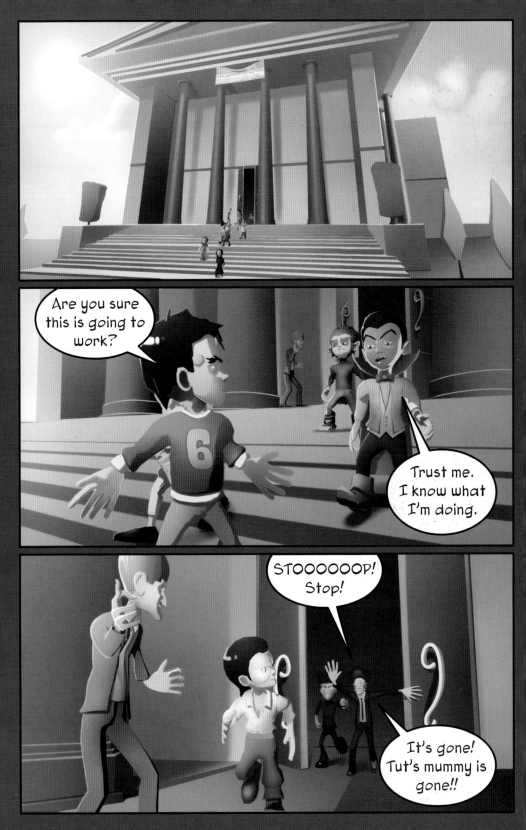

WHO IS
KING TUT?

King Tut's full name is King Tutankhamun. He became king when he was just 8 or 9 years old.

King Tut married his half-sister when he was just 9 years old!

Unlike pharaohs before him, King Tut did not do much for Egypt. However, the discovery of his tomb and all of his treasures has made him the most recognized and famous pharaoh of all time.

King Tut was only 18 or 19 years old when he died. It is not known what caused his death, but many scientists believe he was murdered.

In 1922, Howard Carter discovered King Tut's tomb. More than 3,000 artefacts were found inside.

GLOSSARY

ancient belonging to a time long ago

coffin a container that a person is buried in

curator the person in charge of a museum

exhibit to show something to the public

fainted lost consciousness for a short time

intense very strong

introduce to tell the name of one person to another person

kingdom a country that has a king or queen as its ruler

majesty the formal title for a king or a queen

monuments statues, buildings, or other things that are meant to remind people of an event or a person

pharaoh the title of kings of ancient Egypt

supervision watch

DISCUSSION QUESTIONS

1. The Mighty Mighty Monsters took a school trip to the museum. Where would you like to go on a school trip? Why?

2. The monsters are all part of a special group. If you could be part of any group, what would it be?

3. The monsters helped King Tut escape from the museum. Do you think that was a good idea? Why or why not?

WRITING PROMPTS

1. Which monster do you like best? Write a few sentences explaining why.

2. The monsters helped King Tut and made a new friend. Write about a time when you helped a friend.

3. What happens after the monsters bring King Tut home? Write a few sentences about his life in the real world.

Information books

The Mystery of Vampires and Werewolves
(Can Science Solve?), Chris Oxlade (Heinemann
Library, 2008)

Creepy Egyptian Mummies You Wouldn't Want to Meet!
David Stewart (Gareth Stevens, 2010)

Graphic novels

Dracula (Graphic Revolve), Bram Stoker, retold by
Michael Burgan (Raintree, 2009)

Frankenstein (Graphic Revolve), Mary Shelley, retold
by Michael Burgan (Raintree, 2009)

Mummies!, Kevin Fleury (Powerkids Press, 2012)

Website

learnenglishkids.britishcouncil.org/en/make-
your-own/make-your-monster
Visit this website to create your own monster. You
can also invent your own scary story, dangerous
animal, or superhero.

Mighty Mighty MONSTERS ADVENTURES

Hide and Shriek!
ISBN: 978 1 406 23718 4

Lost in Spooky Forest
ISBN: 978 1 406 23720 7

The King of Halloween Castle
ISBN: 978 1 406 23719 1

New Monster in School
ISBN: 978 1 406 23723 8

Monster Mansion
ISBN: 978 1 406 23721 4

My Missing Monster
ISBN: 978 1 406 23722 1

Monster Beach
ISBN: 978 1 406 24226 3

The Missing Mummy
ISBN: 978 1 406 24227 0

The Monster Crooks
ISBN: 978 1 406 24228 7

The Toy Snatcher
ISBN: 978 1 406 24230 0

The Wolfboy's Wish
ISBN: 978 1 406 24231 7

The Scare Fair
ISBN: 978 1 406 24229 4

They're Fang-tastic!

ABOUT
SEAN O'REILLY
AND ARCANA STUDIO

As a lifelong comics fan, Sean O'Reilly dreamed of becoming a comic book creator. In 2004, he realized that dream by creating Arcana Studio. In one short year, O'Reilly took his studio from a one-person operation in his house to an award-winning comic book publisher with more than 150 graphic novels produced for Harper Collins, Simon & Schuster, Random House, Scholastic, and others.

Within a year, the company won many awards including the Shuster Award for Outstanding Publisher and the Moonbeam Award for top children's graphic novel. O'Reilly also won the Top 40 Under 40 award from the city of Vancouver and authored *The Clockwork Girl* for Top Graphic Novel at Book Expo America in 2009.

Currently, O'Reilly is one of the most prolific independent comic book writers in Canada. While showing no signs of slowing down in comics, he now also writes screenplays and adapts his creations for the big screen.